ANSWERS
TO
YOUR QUESTIONS

ABOUT SHARKS

Hal Scharp

Naturegraph

Library of Congress Cataloging in Publication Data
Scharp, Hal.
    Answers to your questions about sharks.

    1. Sharks—Miscellanea. I. Title.
QL638.9.S27   597'.31   79-13420
ISBN 0-87961-079-4 Paper Edition
ISBN 0-87961-080-8 Cloth Edition

Cover photo by Jack Stein Grove. The Galapagos Shark, *Carcharhinus galapagensis.* Photographed at Tower Island, Galapagos Archipelago.

Books for a better world

Naturegraph Publishers
P.O. Box 1075
Happy Camp, California 96039

To Mary –

Steadfast companion in that vast sea of research, whose multiple roles of wife, proofreader, secretary, and typist made this book possible.

ACKNOWLEDGMENTS

A work dealing with sharks involves considerable research, and I drew upon many sources for information. The individuals I contacted gave their time and material generously. Indeed, without their splendid cooperation, this book could not have been written.

I have received unfailing assistance from the staffs of The Wometco Miami Seaquarium, Miami, Florida; The Narragansett Sport Fisheries Marine Laboratory, Narragansett, Rhode Island; The Shark Research Panel of the American Institute of Biological Sciences, Washington, D. C.; The Smithsonian Institution, Washington, D. C.; The International Game Fish Association; The Woods Hole Oceanographic Institution, Woods Hole, Massachusetts; The International Oceanographic Foundation, Miami, Florida; The U. S. Department of Interior, Fish and Wildlife Service, Washington, D. C.; Sea World, San Diego, California; and Marineland, Marineland, Florida.

I am particularly indebted to "Captains Courageous"—Al Cristy, Frank Mundus, and Les Rayen—who played active parts in helping me with my research, and in landing some of the big 'uns!

A big note of thanks goes to Sevrin Housen, editor, who runs a "tight ship" and provided this attractive format.

Hal Scharp
Homestead, FL

INTRODUCTION

The shark is in the limelight. Whether it intrigues or frightens us, there is no denying that this multimillion-year-old savage possesses a special charisma that inflames our imaginations.

For millenniums man battled the wild terrestrial animals until, at last, he conquered them. Then, as he came to the realization that the sea is indispensable to human existence, he was forced to challenge the oceans and their inhabitants.

Consequently, when he courageously crossed this watery frontier and deliberately invaded the shark's domain, man soon encountered a new threat to his supreme power. Knowing that he could not hope to combat this menace with his limited knowledge of the beasts, he plunged into exhaustive research on sharks.from every conceivable angle. As he pushed against the mysterious veil that shrouds the shark's behavioral motivations and physiological processes, most of the evidence he discovered was contradictory and highly controversial.

Thus, the shark's evil reputation for murdering people, which began with ancient legends and myths, escalated slowly with the accumulation of fragmentary evidence and some substantiated facts, until a terrifying bestseller (and a film that broke all box office records) shocked the world. Since then, and with the advent of *JAWS 2*, millions of shark fans have looked for answers to the age-old questions about this enigmatic, sinister creature.

Although instances exist when humans were chewed, dismembered, quartered, or disemboweled so that they floundered about helplessly in their own blood, most of the confrontations between sharks and people are grossly exaggerated. This is understandable, because our minds cannot conceive of a more horrible fate than to be eaten alive by a monster shark.

There are nearly 250 species of sharks currently roaming the oceans around us. Of this number, only 25 or 30 species are considered dangerous to man. Both the harmless species and the man-eaters are essential to our environment.

Strangely enough, the less sensational, unpublicized aspects of the shark make him a far more incredible and exciting subject than his "killer" image. So far, however, only a few people are aware of the vital roles the shark plays in ecology, recreation, commerce and science.

The shark is a super scavenger—a living vacuum cleaner. In addition to removing all kinds of organic pollution, he rids the seas of sick and injured fish. This helps to control the populations of the leading commerical fishes such as tuna, mackerel, salmon, and herring, and thus ensures that only the healthy stock is perpetuated. A classic example of Darwin's theory that, in nature, only the strong survive.

To the sportsman, the shark represents the ultimate challenge in angling proficiency. The largest "fish" in the ocean, it easily exceeds the weight of the glamorized marlin by a thousand pounds. Yet, its determination and will to live are so strong that even a small three-foot shark will give an angler a surprisingly tough struggle.

The shark's commercial value surpasses that of any other animal because it can be utilized in so many ways. As a live exhibit, it draws hundreds of thousands of awed viewers to marine attractions. Its dead carcass is even more profitable. Its hide is processed into the toughest leather in the world, and even its by-products (teeth, jaws, vertebral discs) are converted into curios and jewelry. The gelatin extracted from shark fins is a staple in Oriental diets; and the flesh, already being consumed by millions of people, could feed starving multitudes all over the globe.

Miraculously, these benefits pale before the shark's significant contributions to medical science. Major breakthroughs in this area have made the shark a champion of mankind! Innumerable research projects have proven that the serums and vaccines derived from shark blood and organs can preserve human life. In fact, the entire body is being used in essential studies dealing with human physiology, immunology, and virology. The possibilities are endless—ranging from treatment of the common cold to fighting deadly carcinoma.

The questions in this book are being asked by everyone who has become fascinated by one of the most primitive, mysterious animals in the world. The answers embody the most recent information gathered from many scientific sources together with my own empirical investigations into the idiosyncracies of this unique, biological engine. I know this book will captivate the reader and satisfy his curiosity about this greatly maligned creature; but, above all, I am confident that the reader will develop a better understanding of the shark and its valid place in man's environment.

CONTENTS

PART II   THE MAN-EATERS

PART I

SCIENCE AND SHARKS

1. Where did the word "shark" come from and what does it mean?

The word has a hazy origin and may have derived from several sources. Prior to 1570, the creature was known in English as *tiburon*, a name taken from the Spanish. But, because of the hostilities between Spain and England at that time, *tiburon* was dropped from the lexicon and was replaced by the German word *schurke* (meaning knave or villain), which gradually evolved into "shark."

2. What good are sharks in nature's master plan?

Although they may appear to contribute nothing, remember that sharks are predators and, as such, fit neatly into the natural scheme of life. They play important roles in controlling the ocean populations and in the removal of unhealthy creatures. For man, they are significant contributors to medical research, commerce, and recreation.

3. When did sharks first appear on earth?

Approximately 250 million years ago. Fossil remains of a species called *Cladoselache* were discovered in the Black Cleveland Shales a few miles from Cleveland, Ohio. This enormously important discovery was made in the 1880's and provided many tangible clues to the puzzling evolvement of sharks and related species.

4. I understand that several species of primitive sharks were quite a bit bigger than our present day sharks and even exceeded the size of our larger whales. What caused their extinction?

Probably the same conditions that caused many other sea and land creatures like the reptiles to become extinct—severe environmental changes that affected their ecological balance. Extreme physical changes in the earth's surface, such as the separation of continents, the formation of huge volcanic mountains, floods, land recession, and underwater volcanic eruptions, all contributed to their demise. Millions of marine and land species gradually perished under these harsh circumstances.

Fig. 1. Whale sharks have little resemblance to whales, except in size; but both creatures do share the same diet of small fish and plankton. Because whale sharks are relatively rare, it is impractical to fish for them on a commercial basis. This specimen measured 37 feet, and was captured off Bimini, Bahama Islands, with only a grapnel anchor and line. Bersol Cox of Bimini poses next to the shark. (Photo by Ralph L. Bowden)

5. What is the largest shark and where is it found? The smallest?

The largest shark species is the whale shark *(Rhincodon typus)*. These huge, lumbering creatures can reach 60 feet, yet are docile and harmless to man. Like whales, they feed only upon small fish and planktonic organisms strained from ocean water. Whale sharks are rarely seen. Enjoying a wide range of distribution, they inhabit offshore waters of the tropical and semitropical oceans of the world.

The smallest sharks are the midwater sharks *(Squaliolus laticaudus)*. The first of these midgets was trawled from the bottom in over 1000 feet of water off the Philippine Islands in 1908. This rare species was mature, cigar-shaped, jet black, and measured slightly under 6 inches.

6. Contemporary literature points to one prehistoric species which might have reached 60 to 80 feet. Isn't that stretching it a little? How was the estimate determined?

Six full-grown men can stand shoulder to shoulder, without being crowded, in the shark jaws hanging in the American Museum of Natural History. The jaws were reconstructed from 5- and 6-inch fossil teeth that belong to *Carcharodon megalodon*, a terrible Goliath that roamed the Miocene seas (12 to 28 million years ago). This species might have reached 80 to 100 feet in length, and was the ancestor of our great white shark *(Carcharodon carcharias)*, which rarely reaches 20 feet.

The reconstruction of the jaws was done to scale, so it was easy to estimate the creature's length. Based upon the recent discoveries of 8-inch teeth, imagine how long the monster must have been. A 100-foot specimen would not be beyond possibility.

7. If I wanted to search for fossil teeth that belonged to the largest shark species, where should I dig?

There are many fossil sites throughout the world but the most productive areas for finding the remains of *Carcharodon megalodon* are in the United States. There is a famous fossil site just outside Bakersfield, California, known as Sharktooth Hill. Also, the estuarine bottoms and high tide lines of the tributaries from Jacksonville, Florida, to Charleston, South Carolina, have produced many good-sized fossil shark teeth. The Myrtle Beach area of South Carolina has provided great pickings for fossil teeth hunters but most specimens of teeth from this area have been badly eroded and are difficult to

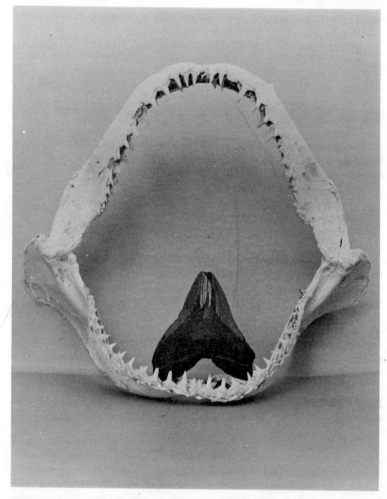

Fig. 2. Put your teeth into this problem! A 5-inch fossil shark tooth compared with the ¾-inch teeth of a present-day lemon shark. The lemon weighed 300 pounds and measured 8 feet. Question: How large was the prehistoric giant? (Photo by Hal Scharp)

identify.

The phosphate pits of Polk County, Florida, have recently produced some mighty fine specimens of fossil teeth belonging to *C. megalodon*. Five- and six-inch teeth are common in local amateur paleontologists' collections. There are even rumors that, with real persistence and determination, still larger teeth can be uncovered in this ancient marine site where, for some strange reason, these gigantic creatures seemed to congregate during the Miocene Epoch, when Florida was buried under 60 feet of water.

8. Why don't sharks possess bony skeletons? Is this some slip-up on the part of nature?

Sharks *do* possess a skeleton of sorts—one made up of cartilage, gristle, and fibers which, in some species, may become calcified with age. Although they have a spinal column, they lack the rib cage found in other vertebrates. At any rate, the bone of contention lies in the way in which sharks evolved.

After 400 million years of evolutionary development, sharks were among a very small number of creatures that were able to adjust and adapt to a harsh and ever-changing habitat—changes that extinguished millions of other life forms. The absence of bony skeletons in sharks is a result of their adaptation, and they *have* achieved a high degree of development.

9. Why do sharks discharge their internal organs while they are hanging either by their tails or mouths?

Since sharks do not have bony skeletons or rib cages, when they are removed from the water and subjected directly to gravity, some of their internal organs slip down.

10. What causes the obnoxious odor that sharks exude soon after they die? Is it present in all dead sharks?

Deterioration in all sharks begins swiftly after death. They develop that offensive ammonia-like odor because of the great amount of urea in their bodies. Also because of the urea, they tend to spoil quickly. Ideally, the flesh should be refrigerated immediately, but if this is impossible, soaking the flesh in brine will remove the odor and prevent decomposition.

11. A friend of mine insists that sharks are not true fishes. If they're not, what are they and how do they differ?

This is going to involve some mind-twisting explanations.

A zoologist, while speaking in a general way about swimming creatures, would probably classify a shark as a fish. But from an ichthyologist's point of view (these are the *real* fish scientists) a shark is *not* a true fish. The difference (and it's a big one) lies in the skeletal construction of each.

Fish, called *Teleosts*, contain a bony skeleton. Sharks, called *Selachians*, possess skeletons made up wholly of cartilage. They belong to the family of *Chondrichthyes* which includes the family of skates, rays, and sawfish, *Batoidei*, that also sport cartilaginous frames. Sharks, skates, rays, and sawfish are also included in a sub-class known as *Elasmobranchs*.

12. How fast can sharks swim and how do they compare with the speed of game fishes?

Most shark species are slow, lumbering, bottom-dwelling creatures. But a few pelagic (open ocean) species exist, such as the mako, great white, blue and porbeagle, whose speeds have been measured at 30 to 40 miles per hour.

Compared to pelagic fishes like the billfishes, tunas, and dolphins (that reach 50 to 60 miles per hour), sharks just don't have it.

13. Do sharks feel pain?

Sharks do not possess the highly sophisticated nervous systems that exist in the higher orders of animals. Therefore, their sensitivity to pain is slight. A case is on record in which a shark was hooked and shot in the head with a .32 caliber revolver. The shark sounded and broke the line. Half an hour later, the same shark, with blood still oozing from its gunshot wound, grabbed a baited hook and was landed. (The tussle was very short, due, no doubt, to loss of blood rather than spirit.)

14. Sharks are a common subject for discussion in elementary schools. Why are our youngsters exposed to creatures whose evil and sinister reputation is based on the terrifying and horrible manner in which swimmers are attacked and killed?

Better remove the pictures of such creatures as lions, tigers, bears (even Smokey!), wolves, and alligators from all their books and keep the kids home from school. Any one of these animals (and I name only a few) is responsible for killing and maiming many more people every year than sharks.

The reason you're hearing more about sharks now is because science has recently uncovered some illuminating facts about these sea-going animals that have put them in the news. Medical research studies are being conducted continuously—probing that mysterious region of their physiology which gives sharks such an enviable advantage over man. The shark is also making substantial contribu-

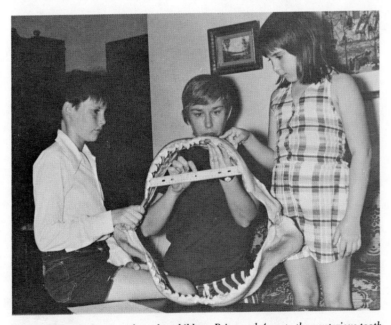

Fig. 3. Judy Johnston introduces her children, Brian and Amy, to the mysterious tooth development of a tiger shark. They are curious about the absence of cavities in the man-eater's dentition, until Mom explains that a systematic tooth replacement process occurs in sharks.

The study of sharks is often included in the curriculum of elementary schools to stimulate the youngsters' interest in marine biology. (Photo by Hal Scharp)

tions to the world food supply, to leather products, and (by providing the evil instruments that put the "bite" on you) to toothy jewelry. Incidentally, they're great sport on rod and reel. *(cont.)*

Fig. 4. Herb Goodman, Lake Worth, Florida, tackle shop owner and shoreline shark fisherman extraordinaire, displays the oddly-shaped head and toothy maw of a 12-foot hammerhead that he landed with rod and reel in the surf. (Photo courtesy Herb Goodman)

Of course, all this might even stimulate a youngster's interest in marine biology. So, is this bad?

15. Why is every zoology student required to study and dissect a shark?

The shark is studied and dissected in school laboratories because it contains most of the physiological characteristics of the vertebrates (including humans).

The spiny dogfish *(Squalus acanthias)* is the species usually chosen for study because they are small and abundant. Thousands of dogfish are dissected every year by students of vertebral taxonomy and zoology. Since dogfish thrive in captivity, they can also be used in a greater range of research that involves advanced studies of immunology or physical disorders of any kind.

16. It's obvious how the hammerhead shark got its name, but why did nature give it such a grotesquely shaped head with eyeballs located on the ends of its stalks?

Who can reason with nature? Her strange mutations in many species of the animal kingdom are often mysterious and inexplicable. Perhaps nature *is* experimenting with this design; and if it proves to be more efficient than her standard models, other sharks will take on similar appearances.

In fact, the freakish shape of its head is advantageous from the standpoint of hydrodynamics. Hammerheads use their flat heads as steering planes. By the movements of their heads in the water, they are able to dive, ascend, and turn more quickly than most other sharks. The location of their eyes actually gives them a wider range of vision when combined with their ability to turn swiftly.

Hammerhead sharks have larger heads than any other sharks, but their mouths are much smaller proportionately. Regardless of the size of their mouths, however, hammerheads are very dangerous and have been responsible for many attacks upon swimmers.

17. Is it true that after a shark loses a tooth another one always pops up to replace it? How is this possible, and why doesn't this occur in fishes or other animals?

Yes, sharks possess a unique, systematic tooth replacement mechanism that never quits. But when teeth are lost, the next teeth in line don't just "pop up" at once. Instead, they move up slowly into a natural biting position.

Most species of sharks have five or six rows of teeth efficiently arranged so that when one is lost or broken off (usually during a heavy feeding frenzy) another will gradually take its place. However, this replacement process continues even if *no* teeth are lost or broken. The active front teeth of a shark are short-lived and will last only 8 to 24 days, depending upon the species. Thus, this remarkable system provides a constant supply of healthy, cavity-free teeth throughout the shark's lifetime. It is conceivable that many thousands of teeth are manufactured and used by a single shark, whose source of biting and crunching equipment operates as long as it remains alive.

When viewing the mouth of a shark, only two front rows of "working" teeth are visible while the remaining ones are lying flat, neatly encased in tough membrane and tissue which supplies nour-

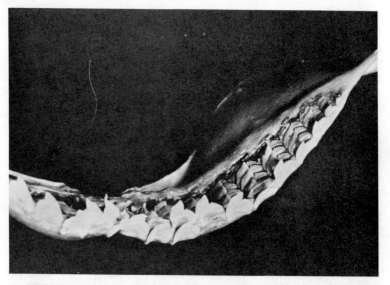

Fig. 5. Part of the jaw structure and teeth of a tiger shark. When the membrane that covers all but the two front rows of teeth is removed, the remaining teeth, in their final stages of development, are exposed. Such an efficient, systematic tooth replacement occurs only in sharks. (Photo by Hal Scharp)

ishment for growth.

Why does this miraculous system exist only in sharks? No one knows. We can only assume that, because the jaw is composed of cartilage instead of the hard bone found in all other vertebrates, the teeth cannot be anchored permanently. Therefore, since the shark must maintain a full set of healthy teeth in order to eat and live, replacement is the obvious answer.

18. Do sharks have venomous glands? Has anyone ever been poisoned by a shark bite?

No known species of sharks possess venomous glands. Neither has poison ever been detected in the countless shark bite wounds that have been examined. However, bacteriologists examining the teeth and mouths of sharks have found a viral strain of bacteria that is pathological to humans. In other words, the mouth of a shark is pretty foul, since it gobbles practically anything that comes along. Naturally, any wound is highly susceptible to infection.

19. Has science ever measured the power of a shark's bite? If so, how great is it?

The power is incredible! Scientists were able to construct instruments capable of measuring the power of the bite of sharks 7 to 10 feet long and discovered, to their amazement, that pressures of as much as 6000 pounds per one-half square inch were exerted.

20. Are sharks plagued with parasitic organisms?

Like fishes, sharks are host to a variety of creatures, but none of the parasites seems to have any lasting effect on the shark's well-being. Due to ever-changing water conditions, leeches are often found in a shark's mouth and, infrequently, in large groups clinging to its rough exterior skin or fins. However, these do not appear to impede the shark's locomotion.

21. How does a shark "home in" on a thrashing hooked fish a quarter of a mile away? Can they actually hear this commotion at such great distances?

Sharks can't *hear* the commotion but they are able to *feel* low frequency vibrations caused by erratic movements in the water. Depending upon water conditons, currents, and the nature and intensity of the movements, they can feel vibrations at considerable distances beyond a quarter of a mile. A shark's basic sensorial mechanism, called the "lateral line system," acts similarly to electronic detection equipment such as sonar. This system, also found in fishes, helps them to locate food.

22. What's all this ballyhoo about a shark being able to sniff a single drop of blood in the water a mile away? That's a lot of water and a lot of baloney, isn't it?

Right. Some literary shark purveyors, like the current ones, are easily carried away. Speaking of the current, let's paddle around with the science of physics for a moment. Imagine, if you will, this same drop of blood (greatly diffused, I agree) carried down-current a mile directly into the zone of a shark's waiting olfactory equipment. And it works beautifully, thank you. Doesn't the "ballyhoo" begin to take on some degree of fact? *(cont.)*

Fig. 6. Portrait of a man-eater! A rare underwater close-up of a fighting-mad tiger shark struggling to free itself from a commercial long-line hook. (Photo by John Debray and Andres Pruna)

Scientists *have* made some astonishing discoveries in this area of research. For instance, scent diffusion in water was measured with some very sophisticated equipment and they found that a shark's nose can detect one part of blood in 10 million parts of water; but that's a lot different from "one drop a mile away."

23. How do scientists discover the mysterious habits and characteristics of sharks, such as their range, distribution, growth rates, and breeding grounds?

Catching sharks, tagging them with an identification number and date, and returning them to the water unharmed will benefit scientific investigators whenever a shark and its tag are recovered. Sharks for tagging are usually caught individually with small baited hooks, but, when a large school is present, a research vessel uses nets to capture them.

A few years ago, Dr. John Casey, marine biologist at the Narragansett Marine Game Fish Laboratory (Narragansett, Rhode Island 02882), instituted an angler-scientist cooperative program which has been extraordinarily successful. Anglers in all parts of the world tag sharks and report the recoveries of tagged sharks. They are informed periodically of the progress and results of the tagging program.

Any angler interested in assisting in this work can write to Dr. Casey, and a tagging kit with instructions will be mailed to him.

24. Do sharks migrate like fishes? What distances do they achieve?

Yes, they do. There are instances when they migrate even farther than some fishes. On the other hand, most sharks remain within a few miles of their birthplaces during their entire lifetimes.

With the scientist-angler cooperative tagging programs, a fairly clear picture of shark migratory and mating habits is now available. This extraordinary portrait proves that one species is able to travel thousands of miles.

Recent shark migratory studies showed that one blue shark, tagged and released 400 miles east of Long Island, New York, was recovered two years later by a Korean long-line vessel off Columbia, South America, almost 2000 miles away. A tiger shark traveled 745 miles in a year and a half; a sandbar covered 868 miles in three and a half months; a black-tipped, 800 miles after 161 days. These figures represent exceptional distances and not the rule.

Studies revealed that over 95 percent of the tagged and recovered sharks ranged much less than 500 miles; in many instances, only 50 to 100 miles was the total range.

Conclusion: very few shark species travel extensively; the majority are strictly stay-at-home characters.

25. I understand that some species of sharks are capable of thriving in fresh water. Does this mean that they are anadromous creatures, sharing the migratory habits of salmon and eels that are able to leave salt water and live for a good while in fresh water?

No, sharks are not anadromous creatures and do not possess the complex mechanism that allows salt water or fresh water fishes to adjust to major changes in their habitats. Many inshore shark species, however, *do* have a strong tolerance for fresh water and make periodic forages up streams and rivers—but only for short periods of time. Some species have reached as far as 150 miles upstream and have even attacked people swimming in fresh water.

You may be referring to the fresh-water shark species, the notorious Lake Nicaragua shark *(Carcharhinus nicaraguensis)* which became trapped by the strange geological phenomenon that took place centuries ago in that area. Their ocean inlet became landlocked, and rains gradually neutralized the salt water. By necessity, they adapted successfully and were able to take up permanent residency. This species is the only authentic fresh-water shark and should not be confused with the bull and the Zambezi sharks (also killers) that share similar physical characteristics, habits, and reputations.

26. Do sharks breed in the same way that fishes do?

There is some similarity in the mating habits of sharks and fishes, but only in rare instances. The vast majority of fishes reproduce in a rather dispassionate manner. The sperm and eggs are deposited independently in the water, and fertilization is accomplished only when the male's sperm happen to drift into contact with the female's eggs. Unfortunately, many eggs are consumed by other fishes or are lost in the current and never fertilized.

Sharks, on the other hand, are more mammalian in their mating habits. Fertilization takes place only by direct intercourse, during which the male injects his sperm into the oviduct of the female.

27. If sharks have sexual intercourse, how does copulation actually take place?

According to the very few, but accurate, reports made by observers who happened upon the scene of this act, copulation took place as males and females embraced by entwining their bodies. The male's role is quite active while the female is passive and usually uncooperative. Thus, the male grasps the posterior edge of one of her pectoral fins in his mouth and manages to flip the female over on her back. Still holding her, he inserts one of his claspers into the lateral pocket of her cloaca and releases his spermatic fluid.

With a female that is "in the mood," the male has no problems. While he and his mate swim side by side synchronizing their move-

Fig. 7.   Female sharks possess only one opening (the cloaca) that serves all excretory and reproductive purposes. The intestines empty through this orifice and so do the kidneys. (The white projection at the base of the cloaca corresponds to the human urethral meatus.) Here, also, the male inserts his clasper during intercourse; later, it is the birth canal for the "pups." (Photo by Hal Scharp)

ments, one of his claspers erects at a right angle to his body and is thrust into the female.

Male claspers are usually equipped with a hooklike spur that holds the cloaca open and the clasper in place until insemination is

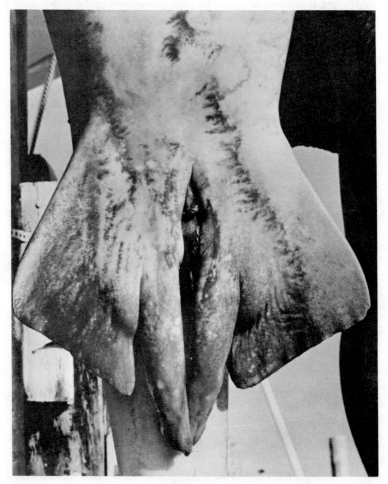

Fig. 8. The external genitals of male sharks are unique in the animal kingdom. They include two penislike appendages called "claspers" that vary in size from species to species. This 7-foot nurse shark's reproductive organs are 8 inches long. (Photo by Hal Scharp)

completed. It has been ascertained that, in some species, copulation has lasted for at least 20 minutes. Although the sexual activities of sharks resemble those of the higher orders of animals, science so far has not been able to determine if sharks experience a climax or orgasm.

28. The external reproductive equipment of a male shark suggests a rather exotic type of sexual activity. Since he is endowed with two copulatory organs, does he use both to impregnate the female? Elucidate, please.

In spite of all the literature about sharks, none has much to offer on this subject. Among the experts there are many conjectures and lengthy suppositions simply because very few persons have actually witnessed sharks *in copulo.* They do agree, however, that sharks' copulatory habits may vary widely among the different species, and that the specific manner in which the sex act takes place depends upon the "whims" of the participants.

The fact that the male shark possesses two claspers (penislike appendages) does not necessarily mean that both are introduced simultaneously into the female oviduct (vaginalike orifice). A few experts claim that double insertion takes place but the majority believe that only one clasper at a time is inserted into the female to complete impregnation.

Undoubtedly, the male's reproductive equipment is the most unusual genitalia in the animal kingdom. Marine biologists suggest that since these creatures of the *Elasmobranch* sub-class (sharks, skates, rays, and sawfish) are results of over 300 million years of evolutionary development, nature, in her wondrous way, has created a foolproof method to perpetuate the species.

29. Is it true that cannibalism among the young takes place in a pregnant shark's uterus before the pups are born? If so, how was this strange phenomenon discovered and what actually takes place?

Yes, the only known cases of intra-uterine cannibalism in the animal kingdom take place in a few shark species. This extraordinary occurrence in the sand tiger shark *(Odontaspis taurus)* was discovered accidentally in 1948 by Stewart Springer, a well-known shark expert, while he was examining a freshly-caught pregnant sand shark.

Springer reported his findings in *Copeia;* and explained, "When I first put my hand through a slit in the oviduct, I received the

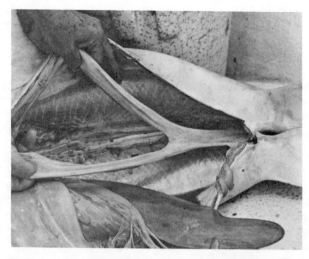

Fig. 9.   The Y-shaped oviduct of a female shark has two remarkable functions. It holds the eggs until they are fertilized, and then converts to a double uterus—the only known twin reproductive system in the animal kingdom. (Photo by Hal Scharp)

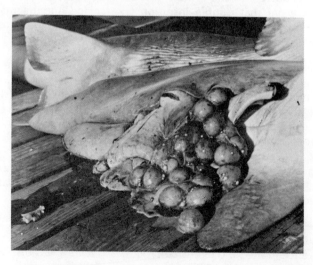

Fig. 10.   A large cluster of yellow, unfertilized eggs from an 8-foot, mature, female nurse shark. Development of the embryos takes place in its twin uteri. Nurse sharks bear as many as a dozen live "pups" after a gestation period of approximately 15 months. (Photo by Hal Scharp)

impression that I had been bitten. What I had encountered was an exceedingly active embryo which dashed about open-mouthed inside the oviduct. The teeth were not strong enough to penetrate my skin but were sharp and hard enough to produce a pricking sensation."

In mature female sand sharks, only the right ovary is functional. Her pea-sized eggs, which are unnaturally small compared to the turtle-sized eggs of most other shark species, number about 15 and pass from the ovary into an area where glands create a thin, but durable, shell-like covering before they continue down into the twin oviducts for fertilization. Only *one* egg in each oviduct hatches an embryo. Both embryos feed upon the other egg yolks for sustenance. As "mom" shark continues to ovulate, the eggs pass down into the oviducts where the two embryos gorge themselves until they reach the astonishing length of about 30 inches (almost one-third the length of their mother). After about 12 months of highly-active existence within the uterus, the two well-formed sharks emerge into the sea with bellies full of their own "brothers" and "sisters."

30. How long do sharks live? Why do they keep dying when in captivity?

No one really knows how long sharks live in their natural environment, although it is generally believed that their life spans are short. Some species, such as nurse sharks and dogfish, have been known to live as long as 25 years in captivity. Others, such as sand and bull sharks, live from 5 to 10 years.

Most species simply refuse to adjust to captivity, and die shortly after capture regardless of their physiological conditions and the extraordinary measures taken to protect them. Scientists speculate that their will to survive is broken when they become disoriented in unnatural surroundings. Because of this sudden change, they often refuse to eat—resulting in self-induced starvation and death.

31. During my last visit to our local marine attraction, I noticed that the sharks don't use their front fins in the same ways that fishes commonly do. Why are these fins rigid and, apparently, non-functional?

Sharks do not possess air bladders to regulate their buoyancy as fishes do. To counteract this lack, they are equipped with rather large pectoral fins which operate only in a vertical position. These are used for steering and planing, allowing sharks to "glide" up or down, while

Fig. 11.   When this 200-pound female nurse shark was dissected, its large, healthy liver was exposed. Shark liver was once the major source of Vitamin A before the vitamin was synthesized in the laboratory. (Photo by Hal Scharp)

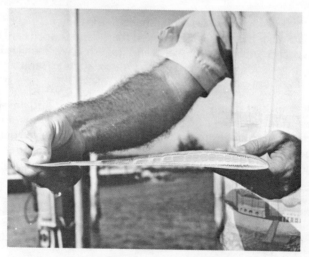

Fig. 12.   The cross section of a lemon shark's pectoral fin. Its shape resembles the air-foil of an aircraft and permits the shark to "plane" through the water with the utmost efficiency. The center cavities contain gelatin—a valuable ingredient from which Chinese sharkfin soup, sharkfin dish, and sharkfin cakes are made. (Photo by Hal Scharp)

their tails provide the main source of propulsion. If you can imagine their pectoral fins operating like the ailerons of an airplane, it is easy to recognize their true function.

32. Since air bladders are absent in all shark species, how do they maintain their buoyancy and stability? Is it true that they must swim continuously so that the water passing through their gills will supply their needed blood-oxygen levels?

Most of a shark's buoyancy is controlled by the amount of oil in its liver. This oil contributes to the flotation factor, but it is not enough to prevent the shark from sinking. Like some of the bladderless fishes (tunas, mackerels, etc.), most sharks must swim continuously to keep from sinking. They achieve stability by using their fins.

A few species of sharks are able to lie motionless on the bottom without any apparent ill effects. The special construction of their gill

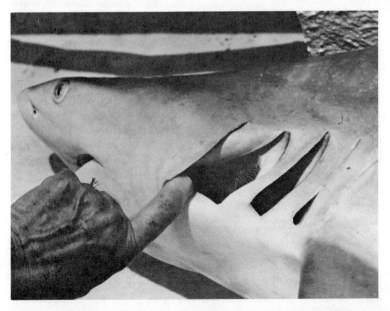

Fig. 13. The gill slit of a lemon shark is pushed aside to reveal the delicate gill-filaments that absorb oxygen from the water and release carbon dioxide. In order to maintain the necessary blood-oxygen level in their systems, sharks swim continuously to force water through their mouths and over the gill-filaments. (Photo by Hal Scharp)

slits allows enough water to pass through their gills for them to extract the necessary oxygen.

33. Why is shark blood used in research? How is it obtained?

Because sharks are known to be virtually disease free, the scientific community wants to know "why." As a consequence, intensive research (chemical and microscopic analyses of shark blood) has led to many amazing discoveries in the last 20 years. Scientists have found that the "infantile proteins" contained in shark blood remain during the entire life of the shark. In human infants, these same proteins that provide immunity to certain diseases disappear shortly after birth. Obviously, further study may prove invaluable to immunologists. In addition, shark blood also contains antibodies, or "immunizing agents," that combat foreign substances in the body. Although sharks produce only *one* of the *three* types of antibodies found in humans, they manufacture ten times as much. By studying these antibodies, medical researchers hope to solve the main complication in organ transplants: the rejection of foreign tissues by the body. There is reason to believe that even more extensive research will provide answers to many perplexing problems involving the treatment of cancer, malaria, and heart disease.

In order to meet the exacting requirements of biological supply companies, specimens of blood must be drawn when the shark is alive. This is done by anesthetizing the shark with MS-222 (Tricaine Methanesulphonate) sprayed in the shark's throat and on its gills. The blood is drawn from the caudal vein, and is either stored in vials or prepared on microscopic slides.

34. What is the "sleeping sharks" theory all about? Do they really sleep?

No. Although the sharks can be almost motionless, their sharp, alert eyes follow the movements of the divers who investigate them.

In the most definitive experiments yet undertaken on this subject, Dr. Eugenie Clark, outstanding ichthyologist and shark expert, made three expeditions to the caves at the northern tip of the Yucatan Peninsula to research "sleeping sharks." Her last trip in 1974 resulted in an extraordinary photographic and narrative report in *National Geographic* (April, 1975).

Dr. Clark's tests showed that the abnormal amount of oxygen in the water of the caves may allow normally active sharks to remain motionless for hours. The lower salt content and the higher acidity and carbon dioxide in the water analysis confirmed her suspicions that fresh water was seeping into the caves. She found that the sharks' parasites were weakened by the lower salinity of the water and, as they relaxed their grips, the remoras had an easier job of cleaning the sharks. Obviously, the remoras could work better when the sharks were motionless. Also, an electro-magnetic field is created when sea water and fresh water are mixed. This, together with the increased amount of carbon dioxide, could cause a feeling of euphoria in the shark.

Dr. Clark concluded that sharks go into the caves to have their parasites removed and stay to enjoy the "high" induced by the carbon dioxide.

35. While watching the many multi-colored fishes in the tanks of our local marine attraction, I occasionally see a rather large shark swim placidly by the viewing window. I notice that several black-and-white-striped fishes, about a foot long, are attached to the apparently unconcerned shark. Are these fishes parasites that will eventually hinder the shark's movements or damage its health?

What you're seeing is a "commensal relationship" between two creatures in which one (in this case, the black and white remoras) benefits greatly from the other without injuring it. A remora's strangely-shaped head has a suction device that allows it to fasten itself to sharks and to other large sea creatures. When a shark slows down to feed, the hitch-hiking remora detaches itself from its host by flexing the louvers of its suction disc, and eats the scraps the shark leaves. The disc doesn't harm the shark nor does its attachment impair the shark's movements or its health; so the remora is not parasitic.

In some instances, when remoras feed upon a shark's parasites, the true commensal relationship changes and the shark benefits, also.

36. In some recent literature dealing with sharks, the attitude of marine biologists who are actually advocating that measures should be taken to preserve the shark population has really shocked me! I simply can't adjust to this line of thought after reading about the horrible way people suffer or die from violent shark attacks. Why should these beasts be preserved if our society is threatened by their presence?

Would you endorse the complete annihilation of the bee population? Camels? Bears? How about hogs and steers? More people (allergy-prone) die from the common bee sting than from shark attacks. Records also show that more camel drivers are trampled into the hot desert sands, and more farmers are maimed while slopping their hogs, than people involved in shark attacks. This also holds true for ranchmen who raise steers. Would you have the grizzly bear, an endangered species, destroyed because of its harm to humans?

Sharks are a vital link in our complex marine ecosystem, and their removal could prove detrimental to the continuity of the food chain. For example, as scavengers, they contribute to the hygiene of the oceanic environment by reducing natural pollution caused by sick or dying fishes. In their role as ocean jackals, sharks are important to the preservation of many ocean species.

Fig. 14.   A "textbook example" of commensalism, a relationship between two creatures in which only one, here the remora, benefits. Several remoras, sometimes called "hitch-hikers," have attached themselves to this sand shark by suction discs on top of their heads. These nonparasitic fishes frequently detach themselves to feed upon their host's dinner. (The fishes below the shark are a species of pilot fish.) (Photo courtesy of Marineland of Florida)

PART II

THE MAN-EATERS

37. What shark species is considered the most dangerous to man, and where is it found?

The great white shark *(Carcharodon carcharias)* tops the list of human exterminators, and, according to case histories, is the most dangerous to swimmers because of its size and aggressiveness. Records reveal that regardless of the defensive measures a swimmer may take, a great white seldom veers off, or is frightened away, once it makes up its mind to attack.

Great whites (called "blue pointers" and "white pointers" in other countries) live in all the oceans and seas of the tropical and temperate zones. Although strictly an oceanic species, they are frequently seen cruising boldly in shallow water, and even in fresh water estuaries. Essentially "loners," great whites are seldom seen schooling.

38. What are some of the other dangerous shark species, and how are they rated as to their likelihood of attacking swimmers?

The United States Navy compiled a list called "Shark Danger Ratings." Each species was rated according to its ferocity, based upon past attack records. A rating of 4+ means maximum danger while a rating of 1+ indicates minimum danger. Although the following species are regarded as the most dangerous, a few species may not have been officially recorded in an attack and, therefore, are not listed or rated.

Great white	4+	Grey nurse	3+	Lemon	2+
Mako	4+	Whitetip	3+	Lake Nicaragua	2+
Ganges River	4+	Porbeagle	2+	Sand	2+
Hammerhead	4+	Tiger	2+	Dusky	1+

Other countries have reported some mighty hostile species that have been responsible for many attacks (some fatal), but they have not been rated. They are: Zambezi, blue, night, thresher, silky, blackfin, black-tipped, sandbar, and Springer's sharks.

39. What are "requiem sharks"?

Requiem sharks represent the family *Carcharhinidae* whose 60-odd species are distributed widely throughout the tropical and temporate zones of the world. The funereal name, *requiem*, was given to this family of sharks because many of its species have a bad reputation for death-dealing attacks.

40. How big was the largest man-eating shark ever caught?

Official records for this are not very clear. Several catches have been reported with incomplete details. There is on record a large great white shark *(Carcharodon carcharias)*, weighing more than 7300 pounds, that was harpooned off the Cuban coast during the mid forties. Although the fish reportedly measured only 21 feet, its liver weighed over 1000 pounds.

Another great white which weighed 4500 pounds was harpooned by Captain Frank Mundus, a famous shark-fishing guide, off Montauk Point, Long Island, New York. That man-eater was probably the largest ever caught off the coasts of the United States.

41. I'm becoming rather weary of reading lurid accounts about a shark's gastonomical diversity and capacity. I just can't stomach the claim that sharks have actually inhaled and digested "a roll of roofing paper, a truck tire, a keg of nails, heads of cows and horses, and 300-pound sea turtles"—to quote only a few of the many highly improbable, non-edible items that writers seem to glory in reporting time after time. Is there really any truth to these gustatory accusations?

We'd better get down to biological cases. To begin with, although the shark is probably one of the most remarkable eating machines around, most of the items you mentioned were not really digested. The shark's stomach is divided into two sections, each with a different function. The articles were probably found in the first section called the "cardiac stomach" that serves as a kind of holding tank for everything ingested. If the contents are acceptable for digestion, the cardiac stomach signals to the second section, called the "pyloric stomach," to open the "gate" and let the food through. Then the pyloric can go to work and reduce it to a nourishing gruel (chyme) before it is released into the intestines for final absorption by osmosis.

42. Why were some of the aircraft used against the Japanese during World War II painted to represent shark jaws, and called the "Flying Tigers"?

This was a ploy that was actually initiated before World War II

Fig. 15.   The "Monster Man of Montauk" frames himself in the 42-inch jaws of a 4500-pound great white shark. Captain Frank Mundus harpooned the extraordinary specimen off Long Island, New York. This shark is probably the largest ever captured in the United States. Mundus served as a consultant during the filming of the movie JAWS. (Photo courtesy of Captain Frank Mundus)

when the Chinese were at war with Japan. Knowing that mythology had instilled a terror of sharks in the hearts of the Japanese, the Chinese deliberately painted a shark's open mouth on their aircraft. Later, a squadron of planes, under the command of General Chennault, was named "Flying Tigers" after the species of sharks known as tiger sharks. The "Flying Tigers" defended the Burma Road, China's supply link with India, from Japanese air power, and, presumably, frightened a few enemy pilots.

43. After reading Peter Benchley's novel, *JAWS*, I couldn't wait to see the movie version. Both the movie and the book were fascinating, but the impact on me was so terrifying that I developed an immediate, intense fear of sharks. Now I'm too frightened to swim at our seaside

Fig. 16. A World War II pilot and his fighter plane. The Chinese, knowing that mythology had instilled a terror of sharks in the Japanese, deliberately painted a shark's open mouth on their aircraft.

Later, a squadron of planes, under the command of General Chennault, was named the "Flying Tigers" after the species commonly known as tiger sharks. (Photo courtesy of U. S. Air Force)

resort. Do sharks really cruise up and down coastal beaches looking for swimmers to eat?

No, sharks are not in the *habit* of dining upon people. Sharks survived long before man evolved; they subsisted before man decided to take his first swim; and they still don't need human flesh in order to live. Occasionally, man just happens to get in their way, and if they're hungry or provoked, they attack. When man intrudes into *their* domain, you can't really blame them.

A look at the official records reveals that although millions upon millions of bathers flock to the sea shore each year, the number of shark attacks is practically nil. Actually, a greater danger exists when a bather leaves his parked car and crosses the road to walk toward the beach. Traffic accidents (which maim and crush, too) far outnumber shark attacks. Incidentally, more people die in the United States from wasp stings than from sharks. (See Question/Answer #50, p. 45.)

44. I've been a deep-sea skin diver for 20 years. In my time I've seen a lot of sharks (even speared a few small ones) and had practically no fear of them. However, after reading *JAWS* and *JAWS 2*, and seeing both movies, I don't mind admitting that now, when I go diving, my hackles spring up at the sight of a 2- or 3-foot shark. What have Benchley and Searls done—conditioned the public into thinking, "don't go near the water"? Now I wonder, was I foolishly taking too many chances?

You've got a lot of company. Hundreds of thousands of skin divers (the figure will be near the million mark soon) are thinking the same thing. Of course, if prospective divers read or see *JAWS* and *JAWS 2*, the figure *might* decline. Many will either develop "aquaphobia," or switch to fresh water and dive among the frogs and lily pads instead.

I'm sure Benchley and Searls weren't trying to spook swimmers and divers. They fictionalized each situation and, with narrative artistry, cleverly wove into it a set of circumstances that resulted in two shocking endings. Although nothing like this has ever happened, it is *not* impossible. This fact, together with the many myths that surround the shark, is enough to strike terror into any swimmer. But look at the odds. Shark attack statistics attest to the obvious improbability of such occurrences.

45. Back in 1916, during a 10-day period in the month of July, five shark attacks occurred within a specific area along the New Jersey coast. Four persons were killed and another badly wounded. Do I

detect the New Jersey "rogue shark" theory as possible background material for Peter Benchley's novel *JAWS*?

Could be. The sinister behavioral pattern of the shark and the geographical location certainly suggest that Benchley recognized the significance of this evidence and utilized it in his novel. With any little-understood animal, in-depth research is necessary to identify and record its habits and personality in order to use it as an important character in any story—fiction or non-fiction. Most experts agree that Benchley did his research well. Naturally, he will be bombarded with questions and ridicule from laymen *and* experts because he chose to fictionalize one of the most controversial animals in the world.

46. What is the "rogue shark" theory and how do people view its sinister implications for swimmers?

Whenever possible, shark attacks are investigated thoroughly by government officials who are trained to ferret out all kinds of information. These specialists actually conduct a criminological study of an attack and its relation to others in the Shark Attack File. Case histories show that some of these investigations lead to suppositions that a solitary, malicious shark may be responsible for a series of attacks upon swimmers or divers.

It has been suggested by the late Sir Victor M. Coppleson, a highly respected authority on shark attacks in Australia, that a shark, after tasting human flesh, will continue to search for similar game. He compared the shark to man-eating tigers and lions that prey only upon people, once they've sampled the genus *Homo*. Coppleson labeled these reputed killers "rogue sharks" and substantiated his theory by thorough investigations and accurate predictions.

But this does not explain all shark attacks. What triggers one attack does not necessarily trigger another. Records show that, statistically, shark attack behavior consists of countless individual peculiarities and idiosyncrasies that characterize the creature as "a very unpredictable animal."

47. From reading about the many fatal and non-fatal shark attacks upon people throughout the world, I find that, in most instances, the investigating authorities can identify the exact species of shark that made the attack. How in the world is this possible?

Each inshore species of man-eating (or man-biting) sharks has its own *modus operandi*. Not all species attack in the same way nor under similar conditions. Some are strictly shallow water villains; others attack only in deep water; and still more do their "dirty work" only in murky water. This is only *one* clue that points to the identities of a few species.

Exact identification of a shark is made from the shape of the tooth marks in the flesh or from tooth fragments found in the bone or gristle of a victim. These marks or fragments are compared with master sets of shark jaws that are indigenous to the area where the attack occurred. Almost every major coastal marine laboratory keeps master sets of jaws specifically for use in shark attack investigations. Although this method of identification has only been used accurately in recent years, it is virtually flawless.

48. Is it true that sharks will deliberately attack a boat in order to get at its occupants?

It is rather doubtful. Most of the records of shark attacks upon boats are sketchy and lack eyewitness accounts.

Sharks *have* attacked occupied boats, but it is suspected that in these instances the sharks were provoked. Most people believe that a solid barrier separating a person from the water and the sharks is enough to discourage sharks from launching some kind of assault.

There is, however, a vivid case of a great white shark attack upon a 14-foot dory carrying two lobstermen off Cape Breton Island, Nova Scotia, in 1953. The brute rammed into the dory, making an 8-inch hole and leaving a tooth embedded in the wooden hull. (The species was identified from the tooth.)

No one seems to know what caused this attack or if it was provoked, but it was responsible for the death of one of the men. Ironically, he drowned when both fishermen were dumped into the icy waters after the impact. The shark, estimated to be 12 feet long, evidently was dismayed by a mouthful of Nova Scotia hard timber splinters, and swam away instead of advancing upon the helpless men.

This incident made headlines, and the tragic drama was later recreated on canvas by Paul Calle, a well-known painter.

49. What is the International Shark Attack File and for what purpose was it instituted?

The Shark Attack File (SAF), a large collection of data on shark attacks, was originally compiled by the Division of Fishes, Smithsonian Institute, Washington, D. C., in 1958. Records of attacks go back as far as 1580. Information concerning past attacks was gathered from every possible source. Several clipping services were used to collect reports of attacks from South African and Australian newspapers. These two regions were, and still are, considered most prone to shark attacks.

Now, each time an attack is reported, investigators make every effort to contact immediately such persons as doctors and policemen who might be able to supply accurate data.

The SAF is located at the Mote Marine Laboratory in Sarasota, Florida. It has been computerized with a set of 87 questions concerning the species of shark, the environmental conditions, the type of wound, how the wound was treated, the kind of activity engaged in

Fig. 17. This wise crew of a commercial shark fishing vessel gives a wide berth to a 500-pound killer as they wrestle it onto the deck. (Photo by Hal Scharp)

by the victim when the attack happened, and many other details relative to the attack.

The purposes of the SAF, as stated by H. David Baldridge, author of *SHARK ATTACK*, are, "to serve as a chronicle of all known shark attacks and to provide source material for identification and study of factors associated with and possibly causatively related to shark attack."

50. How many shark attacks take place throughout the world during a year? What percentage of these are fatal?

According to the Shark Attack File, the average number of world-wide attacks reported in a year is 28. Of these, only about 35 percent (or 10) are fatal. But these are only statistics.

No one really knows how many attacks occur throughout the world, fatal or non-fatal. Authorities agree that more unrecorded attacks (again, fatal and non-fatal) take place every year than recorded attacks.

A casual glance at a map of the world—especially that tremendous area covered by the tropic and temperate zones where man-eaters always exist—reveals what the investigators and record keepers are up against. Thousands of miles of inhabited coastlines along continents, islands, and coastal estuaries contain numberless settlements and communities where even the basic means of communication are absent. In these remote areas, unrecorded and unknown attacks could literally number in the *thousands* every year. Undoubtedly, shark attacks could account for a substantial number of the missing persons from these many undeveloped communities. No one can say how many people are attacked by sharks every year.

51. What was the largest mass shark attack in history, and under what circumstances did it take place?

The largest mass attacks were bloody affairs that occurred during World War II, after the sinking of large vessels which left many survivors adrift at the mercy of marauding sharks. Probably it is not right to single out any one incident as the most tragic as far as shark attacks are concerned.

Literally hundreds of big vessels, filled with crews and troops, were sunk in the tropic and temperate zones of the world where sharks abound. In each allied and enemy sinking, the number of men who were killed or injured by sharks was never known, because it was impossible to verify the number who went down with their ships or were wounded and died in their life jackets before being attacked. But we *do* know that there were thousands of men attacked by sharks during the war years.

One tragic sea disaster occurred when the cruiser *Indianapolis* was torpedoed and sunk by a Japanese submarine in the Philippines. Only 316 men survived the sinking and the four horror-filled days and nights that followed. After the rescue, it was determined that 883 men had died, most of them in the water. Of these, 88 recovered bodies had been mutilated by sharks. Of the 316 who survived, many were attacked by sharks but managed to remain alive until help came.

52. What does a "feeding frenzy" among sharks mean?

This is a feeding pattern of a group of competitive, voracious sharks whose moblike behavior churns the water into a froth as they strike at any moving object.

53. Is it true that authorities caution female bathers against entering the water if they are menstruating?

Yes, it is true, although they admit that there are no statistics to back them up. To my knowledge, there have been no tests conducted on menstrual blood as a shark attractant. This raises a supposition that the chemical composition of menstrual blood may differ so drastically from fresh blood that sharks *could* be unresponsive. Again, there are no statistics to prove that open wounds will invite shark attacks, but the experts still advise against swimming with wounds of any kind.

Women can take heart from the fact that the odds are in their favor. In all the coded attacks from the Shark Attack File, 93 percent were male (13.5 male victims for each female). Although more men than women engage in water activities, in the cases of attacks connected with recreational activities at or near beaches, the victims were still predominantly male.

54. How are bathers protected against shark attacks along the heavily populated beaches of large municipalities?

Shark fences made of rigid metal were the earliest form of protection. Although they are very impractical for large stretches of beach,

because erosion and shifting sand make the cost of maintenance pro-
hibitive, some fences are still in use in Australia and South Africa to
protect small swimming areas.

"Meshing" of beaches is now the most effective means of protect-
ing bathers. Staggered rows of gill nets are secured in the sea beyond
the offshore breaker line. There have been cases in which sharks
slipped in between the nets but were caught on the way out.

Many beaches employ guards, not only to help swimmers in dis-
tress, but also to watch constantly for sharks. Aircraft spotting has even
been employed occasionally by some affluent communities.

**55. What is the most successful shark repellent presently used by the
military services?**

Unfortunately, there is little available to repell sharks. Science
just hasn't been able to cope with the problem successfully.

The Navy-developed repellent called "Shark Chaser" is still being
issued to members of the armed forces and offered for sale on the
civilian market, despite mounting evidence that it is far from being 100
percent effective.

A 6-ounce packet of Shark Chaser contains 4½ ounces of black
dye, 1½ ounces of copper acetate and a soluble binder which holds
the two together. The binder dissolves in water over a 3 to 4 hour
period.

Research indicates that the copper acetate is not effective as a
chemical deterrent, so any possible value must be in the black dye.
Laboratory studies have shown that some species of dangerous sharks
enter deeply-dyed water with reluctance, but other species swim right
through it. Scientists conjecture that a dyed area of water may seem
like a solid barrier to sharks.

It is assumed that the reason Shark Chaser is still being supplied is
because there isn't anything better available.

56. If I'm in the water and I see a shark in the area, what should I do?

Shark attack experts and investigators who have compiled data
based upon the Shark Attack File records recommend the following:

1. Never provoke or molest a shark, regardless of its size or possible

disposition.

2. Shout for help and leave the water as soon as possible even if the shark doesn't seem to be interested in you. Use smooth, even movements and make no unnecessary splashing or turbulence.

3. If you cannot leave the water, remain submerged and watch the shark so that you can counter a possible attack.

4. If an attack is imminent, don't panic; use *any* weapon or object to fend off the shark. Use a club, spear, or knife—without trying to kill or wound it. Offensive attacks upon a shark with a power-head, spear gun, or knife may only provoke it.

5. Aggressive movements may have two different effects. The shark may consider them a threat and attack, or it may be startled into retreating.

6. If contact is made, fight. Do anything! Poke its eyes and gills, shout, blow bubbles. Strike with your bare hands as a last desperate measure. These have worked in some cases and might gain time during which the shark may leave or you may be rescued.

7. If possible, try to control any bleeding yourself until help arrives. Even then, rescuers should make every effort to control bleeding *before* trying to reach shore.

PART III

SHARKS AND COMMERCE

57. Why do so many people, especially in the United States, have a strong aversion to eating shark meat?

For the same reason that multitudes of people refuse to try rattlesnakes, snails, and eels—because the public has been conditioned to think of them as repulsive, inedible creatures.

Because sharks usually attack helpless, unsuspecting people, they have come to represent foul play and death. Therefore, it is reasonable for people to shudder at the thought of eating *them*. Until

Fig. 18. Cooked shark meat is white, firm and tasty. The portion between the head and the dorsal fin is the choicest area to obtain steaks for broiling. (Photo by Hal Scharp)

the present, very little has been done to reveal shark meat as an appetizing, nutritious, and tasty food. No advertising campaigns extolling the virtues of shark meat have been attempted.

Rattlesnakes, snails, and eels are tolerated because a few daring souls tried them, found them delicious, and spread the word. But that's the end of it. Most people are *still* turned off! Years ago, lobsters and a few other species of bottom scavengers were also avoided until advertising and the news media made them the gourmet fare they are today.

A recent example of what good publicity can do is the king crab. This huge, horny, spiderlike apparition that measures up to 6 feet across in icy Alaskan waters had few buyers until about a decade ago when its name was changed from spider crab to king crab. After some intensive advertising, sea food lovers all over the world discovered that the succulent white meat encased in those long legs is a palatable delight.

58. I think I've been "had." Last night I took my date to a Chinese restaurant and ordered the works, including two bowls of sharkfin soup. My bill came to 32 dollars and 50 cents! When I asked the waiter why two simple dinners cost so much, our language difference got in the way, but his explanation seemed to concern the soup. I gave up, paid the bill, and left. What in the world was he trying to tell me about the soup? Is it *that* expensive?

You bet! In the first place, shark fins are hard to come by. Sharks are in such great demand in the Orient that thousands of pounds of sun-dried fins are imported from the United States each year. They undergo a special process to extract the gelatin, the expensive ingredient that flavors and gives body to sharkfin soup, sharkfin dish, and sharkfin cakes. Dried fins bring over 7 dollars a pound in the United States!

By eating a bowl of sharkfin soup, you were partaking of the food of the Chinese gods. At one time, it was served only to royalty. The recipe, an ancient, complex one requiring many other ingredients, such as stock and spices, is time-consuming and, therefore, expensive. Today it's nothing to pay 8 or 9 dollars for a bowl of the stuff. So relax. You "had" it, all right—nothing less than royal epicurean treatment!

59. According to some religious doctrines, eating fish that have

smooth skins and no scales is strictly prohibited. Are sharks included under this precept?

Any theologian will tell you that these dietary laws were enacted originally to ensure the purity of food. Yet these ideas still persist regarding catfish, for example, even though we know this fish is not detrimental to our health.

However fine and smooth they may feel when the skin is stroked near the tail, sharks possess scales. Stroking a shark's skin from tail to head is like rubbing sandpaper. (It is actually used as an abrasive called "shagreen" by cabinetmakers.) Their placoid scales are much different in structure from those of the bony fishes. Under magnification, the scales appear as sharp projections that are also known as dermal denticles. Physiologically, these are real, permanent *teeth* containing a dentine surface and a central pulp canal composed of blood vessels and nerves. *(cont.)*

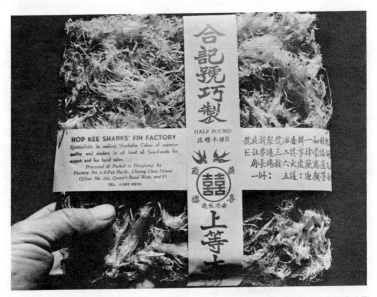

Fig. 19. Have you priced a bowl of sharkfin soup recently? The Hop Kee Sharks' Fin Factory of Hong Kong, specializes in converting the gelatin from shark fins into a dried noodlelike substance. This one-half-pound package sold for 9 dollars in 1978 in Miami, Florida. No wonder Chinese restaurants commonly charge 8 to 9 dollars for one serving of the delicacy! (Photo by Hal Scharp)

So where do we stand from a theological viewpoint? Sharks were around long before the Old Testament was written. Were they known as scaleless or scaled sea creatures then? Zoologists call them "scales." Will a theologian today agree and interpret them as such under the religious restrictions? I think so.

60. I understand that the commercial shark fishing industry is gradually swinging upward after a long recession caused by the development of synthetic Vitamin A. What are sharks worth today?

Just to give you an idea, we'll start where the top dollar is. To begin with, sharks are more valuable as live, healthy specimens on exhibit at marine attractions. Curators sometimes spend thousands of dollars to get a healthy shark shipped to their compounds. There's big money in it, if facilities and market contacts are combined with the most important ingredient: the know-how to keep the sharks alive in captivity.

Most of the industrial revival, however, is concentrated in catching sharks for the value of their commercial components. Hides in good condition bring anywhere from 10 dollars for a 6-footer to 30 dollars for a 10-footer. Dried fins, always in great demand in China, Japan, and other oriental countries, sell for about 7 dollars a pound. The flesh, too, is a good source of income, if adequate refrigeration facilities are available and distributors can guarantee a steady market. Properly cleaned and refrigerated sharks will earn as much as 35 cents a pound for the fisherman.

Coastal gift shops and skin diving headquarters will always buy jaws and teeth. A 6-inch shark jaw, meticulously cleaned, sells for about 5 or 6 dollars; a 12-inch jaw, about 25 dollars; a 24-incher, as much as 200 dollars! Hundreds of individual teeth are used in the jewelry industry. Some, when gold-plated, cost more than the finest costume jewelry.

61. I notice that many top-of-the-line leather goods manufacturers are using substantial amounts of sharkskin. How expensive are sharkskin products, why are they in such demand, and what species of sharkskin is the most popular?

Western-style boots retail for 75 to 100 dollars, depending upon the quality of the stitching and decoration. Dress shoes sell for 50 to 75 dollars. Belts usually go for 20 to 25 dollars, while a wallet costs 25 to 35 dollars. *(cont.)*

Sharkskin is held in high esteem, not only because of its durability (it will outlast any other leather), but also because it is exceedingly attractive. The handsome grain of the tiger shark makes it the most popular skin for leather products.

62. Why are shark leather products so expensive?

Shark leather is one of the toughest leathers known. After the shark's skin has gone through a complex tanning process to turn it into leather, it becomes soft, pliable, and unbelievably durable. Articles fashioned from this leather will not only outwear other materials but will also retain their shape and fresh appearance much longer. Shark leather is especially useful in boots and shoes because of its scuff-proof qualities.

The United States Government Bureau of Standards put shark leather through its rigid official tests and found that it contains a tensile strength of almost 7000 pounds per square inch. In comparison,

Fig. 20. Shark leather makes some of the most durable, attractive, and expensive products available. Wallets and belts start at 20 dollars; shoes at 50 dollars; and boots at 75 dollars. (Photo by Hal Scharp)

cowhide tested at about 5000 pounds per square inch.

63. I know that sharks, one of the most difficult creatures to keep alive in captivity, die at an alarming rate. How do the aquariums and marine attractions throughout the world manage to keep a steady quantity of live sharks for display in their tanks?

Hundreds of live sharks of many species and sizes are shipped all over the world annually, at great expense and effort. Since a shark's longevity (especially in captivity) is short, specimens must be caught and transported continually to provide a supply for viewing purposes in aquariums.

Many coastal marine attractions catch their own sharks. They maintain and operate shark fishing and transportation equipment, not only to save costs, but to ensure a constant stock of sharks for exhibition.

Fig. 21. Dave Powell, right, curator of Sea World, San Diego, California, and his assistant hook and hand-line a blue shark in the Pacific Ocean prior to hauling it aboard. The chute was designed specifically to minimize injury to the shark and to facilitate easy landing operations. (Photo courtesy of Nancy Chase, Sea World)

Fig. 22. (Above) *Powell and his assistant proceed to pull the thrashing shark up the chute and into the canvas tank. (Photo courtesy of Nancy Chase, Sea World)*

Fig. 23. (Below) *Powell places a respiratory mouthpiece into the mouth of the immobilized shark. The device was designed to provide life-giving oxygen while the valuable specimen is being rushed to one of the tanks at the marine attraction. (Photo courtesy of Nancy Chase, Sea World)*

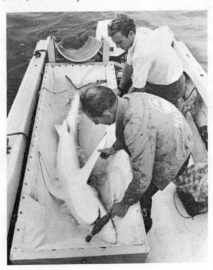

Fig. 24. The shark is released in a plastic-lined outdoor exhibition tank—to the delight of the intent customers. The lining is for its protection. Since sharks are stunned and almost in shock after capture, they swim about the tanks in a disoriented fashion and may injure themselves by bumping into concrete walls. (Photo courtesy of Nancy Chase, Sea World)

64. Why are sharks featured on the postage stamps of many foreign countries?

Some countries, recognizing that sharks' beneficial attributes outweigh their bad points, and knowing the value of sharks to the economy of their peoples, readily honor the subject on postage stamps.

Fig. 25. In some countries, sharks are important enough to be featured on postage stamps. The one on the left, the Lake Nicaragua species, is a killer responsible for many attacks upon the natives. The basking shark on the right is a huge, docile, harmless creature that is valued only for its commercial use. (Photo by Hal Scharp)

PART IV

FISHING FOR SHARKS

65. Do sharks have any enemies?

Yes, they do. One of their worst, and most frequent enemies is other sharks, even of their own species. Sharks dine upon sharks whenever the opportunity arises. A wounded shark is especially vulnerable to immediate attack by its companions, with predictable results. Even pregnant females, if they're hungry enough, will try to gobble up their young, tender offspring as soon as they deliver a litter.

Sharks caught napping in the deepwater habitat of the giant squid (especially the Pacific Ocean species commonly found along the Humboldt Current off South America) are in real trouble. A huge 50- or 60-foot squid can easily grab a 1000 pound shark with its tremendous tentacles. The tentacles, with hundreds of huge suction discs, draw the writhing victim up to the sharp, formidable beak with which the squid devours the helpless shark—piece by piece!

Porpoises also will stand for no nonsense from sharks, especially if one or more sharks invade the privacy of a female porpoise while she is giving birth to her young. Groups of socially-oriented porpoises always maintain an organized vigil over the intimate ordeal of birth, and do not hesitate to bombard the underbelly of an over-curious shark with swift blows until its internal organs are crushed and the predator sinks helplessly down, writhing in its death throes.

Orca, the killer whale, can be a nasty enemy of the shark, but, as a rule, both go about their own business and avoid any kind of confrontation.

Man has been, and still is, an enemy of the shark. He has contributed significantly to their gradual decimation by killing them for commercial use and for sport.

66. Do any of the large billfishes such as swordfishes and big black marlins ever attack a shark?

Yes, but only for defensive reasons. Billfishes have been observed rushing a shark that has attacked them. Broadbill swordfishes, favorite quarry of the dreaded and swift mako shark, have often been forced to stand their ground and fight by thrusting their bills into fearless, hungry makos much larger than themselves. *(cont.)*

Fig. 26. Captain Charles Buie, collector for the Miami Seaquarium, points to the evidence of an unusual encounter between a sailfish and a bull shark. The wound had healed and the shark was healthy when it was captured. By the size of the bill, the sailfish was estimated at only 50 pounds, yet it had the courage to charge and repel the attack of a 300 pound adversary. Buie had exhibited the live shark for several days when it died, cause unknown. (Photo by J. W. LaTourrette, courtesy of Wometco Miami Seaquarium)

A rather intriguing case is on record in which a relatively small, 50-pound, Atlantic sailfish defensively clobbered a 300-pound bull shark. The sharp bill broke off and remained embedded in the head of the shark. Surprisingly, the shark survived the attack, was later captured, and was displayed at a marine attraction. The sailfish, presumably, managed to evade the shark and is probably still living, minus most of its bill.

67. Why does the commercial fishing industry in the United States turn up its nose at sharks while foreign vessels cross vast oceans, at great expense, to catch them?

Somebody likes to eat sharks more than we do! Let's face it, we have been conditioned not to eat shark meat simply because we're spoiled. The United States is fortunate to have a wide range, and almost unlimited amounts, of oceanic victuals in its local waters. *(cont.)*

Fig. 27. Like modern-day versions of old-time whalers, Irish commercial shark fishermen tow a good day's catch of basking sharks home. These 30- to 40-foot behemoths will be slaughtered and their oil rendered after they reach port. (Photo courtesy of Irish Tourist Board)

In contrast, many foreign commercial fishing industries, by over-fishing and disregarding the need for conservation management, have depleted their own supply of the seafoods Americans enjoy every day. So they learned to catch sharks and sell the meat to eager, hungry customers. Since little else is available in that price range, shark has become one of their leading foods from the sea. The renowned British snack (fish 'n chips) made from shark meat, is a good example.

Now even the shark populations of these countries are being reduced, and their fishermen must travel great distances to catch our unwanted sharks.

68. What species of sharks are considered game fishes and what are the world record weights of each species?

As of January 1, 1977, the IGFA (International Game Fish Association) recognized six species and one family:

Blue shark *(Prionace glauca)*   410 pounds.
Hammerhead shark *(Sphyrnidae)*   703 pounds.
Porbeagle shark *(Lamna nasus)*   465 pounds.
Mako shark *(Isurus oxyrinchus)*   1061 pounds.
Thresher shark *(Alopias vulpinus)*   739 pounds.
Tiger shark *(Galeocerdo cuvieri)*   1780 pounds.
Great white shark *(Carcharodon carcharias)*   2664 pounds.

69. How large is the official world rod and reel record shark? How about the unofficial record?

A great white shark that weighed 2664 pounds was caught in the waters of the Great Australian Bight in 1959 by Alfred Dean on 130 pound test line. The International Game Fish Association recognizes it as an official world record.

Great white sharks weighing 4000 pounds *have* been caught on rod and reels by anglers but they were either mutilated by other sharks or the landing procedures employed were not in accordance with IGFA rules and regulations. Consequently, the catches were disqualified and ineligible for official recognition.

70. In your opinion, what was the greatest angling feat ever recorded involving a shark on light tackle?

Bob Dyer's 1068 pound great white shark caught off the coast of Australia in 1957 on 20 pound test line! Since the ratio of line test to the weight of the shark is slightly greater than 50 to 1, Dyer needed all the skill and endurance he could summon to boat this shark on tackle so light that it almost defied the laws of physics.

This IGFA record will probably remain unbroken for many years to come.

71. What woman angler made the largest official shark catch on rod and reel, and what did it weigh?

Fig. 28. *Alfred Dean, the "dean" of shark fishermen, with his official World Record great white shark. The monster weighed 2664 pounds and was caught in 1959 on 130 pound test line. (Photo courtesy of Australian News and Information Bureau)*

Fig. 29. *A masterful angling feat! Clive Green of Australia is dwarfed by his 3417 pound great white shark. This killer, caught on 130 pound test line, is the largest "game fish" ever caught on rod and reel. (Photo courtesy of Ande Line Co.)*

Fig. 30. Dolly Dyer, one of the outstanding women anglers in the world, radiates pride in her IGFA Women's Division World Record tiger shark caught in 1953. The monster, weighing 1314 pounds, established a record that still remains unbroken. (Photo by Bob Dyer)

Dolly Dyer, one-half of Australia's famous theatrical entertainment team, and wife of Bob Dyer, the world famous shark angler, holds more shark records than her husband. Mrs. Dyer, one of the outstanding women anglers in the world, holds the International Game Fish Association Women's Division World Record for a 1314 pound tiger shark she caught in 1953. This was a terrific angling achievement —a record that still remains unbroken after all these years.

72. While I was admiring a friend's mounted shark the other day, I noticed that the body surface was smooth and not at all like the rough surface of a live specimen. Don't taxidermists use the skin of a shark when they prepare it for mounting?

No. Because of the highly complex and costly methods required to preserve shark skin, taxidermists reproduce the shark (without the original skin) by a molding process. The real teeth and jaws, however, are used in the finished mount.

73. What is the safest and most effective method to immobilize or dispatch a large, hooked shark while it is in the water alongside a boat?

Shark guns (also known as "bangsticks" or "powerheads") are by far the most effective device to put a shark out of commission. This equipment was designed specifically to kill sharks and to take the place of conventional firearms. Its function is simply to force gas and pellet shot and/or slugs into a point anywhere near the brain or along the length of the spine. This causes instant paralysis of the shark's nervous system.

The "gun" consists of a long pole with a short firing chamber mounted at one end. Depending upon the operator's preference, there are several models available. Some can accommodate 12 gauge shotgun shells and others are designed to fire a variety of high-powered slugs. All models are supposed to operate only underwater.

In actual practice, it is the end of the chamber, thrust forcibly against the shark's body while it is underwater, that triggers the detonation and causes the explosive action within the flesh.

Although high-powered rifles have been used with some success before the inception of the shark gun, they were seldom effective if the slug had to enter the water first. Because of deflection and poor impact power, only a direct shot to the brain had maximum effect.

74. I've often read that to catch small sharks for sport I should simply cruise the shallows and look for sharks foraging for food. And after I spot one, I should cast a bait or lure and he'll gobble up the offering because "sharks are not finicky eaters." Baloney! Every one I cast to spooks off the flats like a scared rabbit running ahead of buckshot! What gives?

Your information was incomplete, failing to mention that in very shallow water even sharks are cautious. In the first place, any creatures cruising about a flat during a falling tide are not exactly hunting for food. They'll do this on an incoming tide or flood tide, but not when they're rubbing their bellies on the bottom looking for a way out to deeper water. Naturally, if you're going to lob a bait or create some kind of commotion near them, they'll split. You've been unlucky in sharking on a dead low or falling tide. Try your luck on the incoming or flood tide.

75. I've heard some wild stories about sharks weighing over 1000 pounds being caught from piers and jetties, but I thought that a boat was always necessary. Can extra-large sharks really be caught and landed safely in this manner?

It's anyone's guess just *how* safe it is to tangle with and land any sized shark from a pier, let alone a 1000-pound man-eater. Still, it's being done all over the world, and not with cable set lines, either, but with rod and reel.

One well-known group of sharkers, the Durban Shark Angling Club of South Africa, has been practicing this for years. They've hooked and landed many large great white sharks (called blue pointers in their waters) weighing more than 1000 pounds, by using a specially-designed reel and rod while fishing from a jetty made from jagged pieces of concrete blocks. This is a live-wire group of sharkers who are really gung ho about the sport *only* when the fishing is done from a pier, or other stationary object, rather than from a boat.

And then there is the case of Walter Maxwell of Charlotte, North Carolina. . . .He caught his world record tiger shark, the largest fish ever caught in North America, from a pier at Cherry Grove, South Carolina. The brute weighed 1780 pounds.

COMMON SHARKS CONSIDERED TO BE DANGEROUS

(See #38 for U. S. Navy "Shark Danger" Ratings)

Name	Max. Size	Appearance[1]	Habitat[2]
Dusky Shark	14 ft.	Blue or leaden gray back	Offshore: tropical and warm temperate waters on both sides of Atlantic
Ganges River Shark	7 ft.	Gray back	Offshore: Indian Ocean to Japan; & ascends freshwater rivers
Gray Nurse Shark	10 ft.	Pale gray back; long upper tail	Offshore, inshore: Australia
Hammerhead Shark	15 ft.	Ash gray back; flat, wide head	Oceanic, offshore, inshore: warm temperate zone of all oceans including Mediterranean Sea
Lake Nicaragua Shark	10 ft.	Dark gray back	Freshwater species of Lake Nicaragua
Lemon Shark	11 ft.	Yellow brown back; broadly rounded snout	Inshore: western Atlantic, northern Brazil to North Carolina, Gulf of Mexico, tropical West Africa
Mako Shark	30 ft.	Deep blue gray back; pointed snout and slender form	Oceanic, offshore: tropical and warm temperature belts
Porbeagle Shark	12 ft.	Dark blue gray back; conical head and pointed snout	Oceanic, offshore: continental waters of North Atlantic; allied forms in North Pacific, Australia, and New Zealand
Sand Shark	10 ft.	Bright gray brown back; dorsal fins nearly same size	Offshore: Indo-Pacific, Mediterranean, tropical West Africa, South Africa, Gulf of Maine to Florida, Brazil, Argentina
Tiger Shark	30 ft.	Gray or brown back; short snout; sharply pointed tail	Oceanic, offshore, inshore: tropical and sub-tropical belts of all oceans
White Shark	30 ft.	Salty brown to black back; blunt snout	Oceanic, offshore: tropical, sub-tropical, especially in western Atlantic and Australian waters
Whitetip Shark	13 ft.	Light gray to slate blue back	Offshore: deep, tropical, and sub-tropical waters, Atlantic and Mediterranean.

SOURCE: *General Principles of Diving.* U. S. Navy Manual

[1] All sharks listed are of some shade of white on the underside.
[2] Habitat is general and may vary.

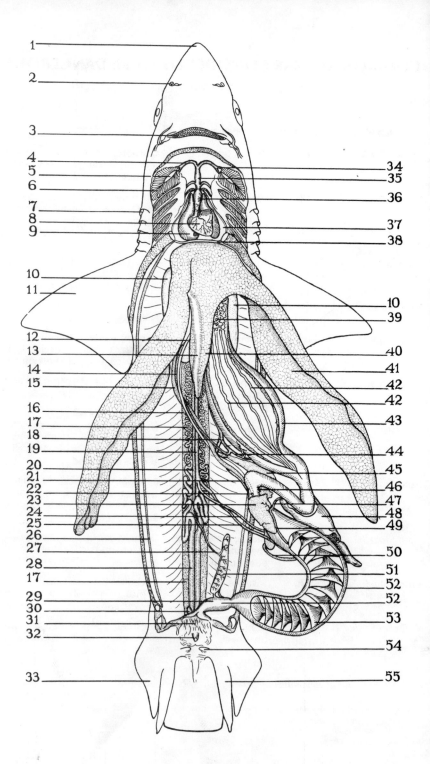

KEY TO ANATOMY OF A SHARK

1. Rostrum
2. Nostril
3. Mouth
4. Anterior branch of ventral aorta
5. Internal gill slit
6. Gill
7. External gill slit
8. Ventricle
9. Atrium, or auricle
10. Testis
11. Pectoral fin
12. Bile duct
13. Gall bladder
14. Hepatic artery
15. Hepatic portal vein
16. Kidney
17. Mesonephric, or Wolffian, duct
18. Coeliac artery
19. Dorsal aorta
20. Posterior cardinal vein
21. Pancreatico-mesenteric artery
22. Opening of bile duct
23. Ventral pancreas
24. Gastrosplenic artery
25. Superior mesenteric artery
26. Lateral abdominal vein
27. Inferior mesenteric artery
28. Seminal vesicle
29. Large intestine
30. Sperm sac
31. Cloaca
32. Urogenital papilla
33. Pelvic fin
34. Afferent branchial artery
35. Ventral aorta
36. Conus arteriosus
37. Pericardial cavity
38. Transverse septum
39. Papillae of stomach
40. Median lobe of liver
41. Left lobe of liver
42. Rugae of stomach
43. Cardiac stomach
44. Gastric artery
45. Dorsal lobe of pancreas
46. Pyloric stomach
47. Anterior splenic vein
48. Spleen
49. Anterior mesenteric vein
50. Posterior intestinal vein
51. Rectal gland
52. Small intestine
53. Spiral valve
54. Abdominal pore
55. Clasper

Opposite) *Sharks play an important role in zoological studies. Unique aspects of their physiology give clues to new medical and commercial uses. (Courtesy of General Biological, Inc.)*

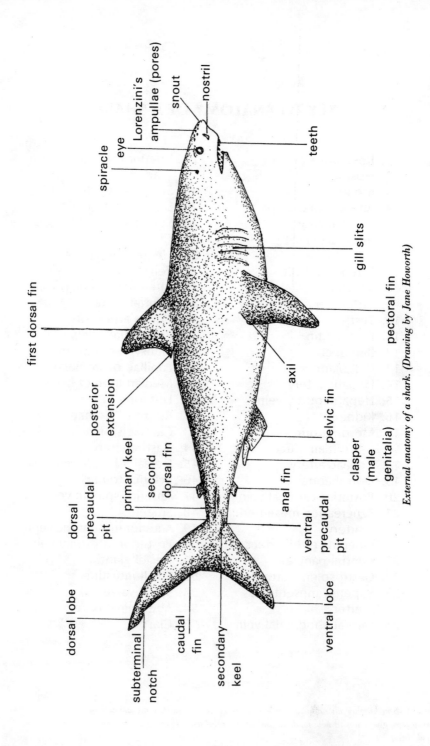

External anatomy of a shark. (Drawing by Jane Howorth)